chris
cartoons

AXOLOTL PUBLICATIONS

AXOLOTL PUBLICATIONS

This collection first published in 1989
by Axolotl Publications
3 Stormyhill Road, Portree, Isle of Skye IV51 9DZ

The individual cartoons first published by
the *West Highland Free Press* between 1979 and 1989

Copyright © Chris Tyler

Printed by West Highland Publishing Company Limited,
Industrial Estate, Broadford, Isle of Skye IV49 9AP

ISBN 0 9514685 1 0

Here is the second selection of my cartoons from the **West Highland Free Press**.

As the **Free Press** prints on a Wednesday evening, I normally draw the cartoon on Wednesday afternoon, by which time the main news stories are evident. However, when you are stormbound on a clam-diving boat in Leverburgh or Loch Uskavagh, even if you do the cartoon on Monday, getting it to Broadford in time can become an epic adventure . . .

I'd like to thank the many friendly lorry drivers, fishing skippers, piermasters and even pilots, without whom there would be a lot of blank pages in this book! And of course everybody at the **Free Press** — without whose encouragement and patience there would have been no books at all.

*For
Jackie, Joe,
James, Douglas
and Beatrice.*

COLDEST WEEK ON LOCAL RECORD

Not even local government offices were immune to the climate. Skye and Lochalsh district councillors were sitting down to deliberations in the environment committee at 11.20am on Monday, when the sound of a Niagaran rush of water from outside the room sent them hurrying into the corridor. A burst pipe of mammoth proportions was threatening to immerse the building, elected representatives and all.

"Next on the agenda, ladies and gentlemen — burst pipes."

15.1.82

"Gentlemen! I said, Any other business?!"

Council set new record

Probably the fastest-ever meeting of the full Skye and Lochalsh District Council took place on Monday morning!

After all of the committees had completed their business, council chairman Willie Nicolson reminded members that they had an appointment at 1.00pm in the Royal Hotel, Portree, with officials from the Solid Fuel Advisory Service. The time was then 12.45pm.

With Councillor Nicolson at the reins, the council hurdled no less than 13 items on the agenda, in the marvellous time of six-and-a-half minutes — an average of 30 seconds per subject!

24.10.80

SMOKERS WIN THE DAY IN COUNCIL DEBATE

Comhairle nan Eilean decided last week to have no policy on smoking. A scheme which would have designated some areas of council premises "no smoking" areas was thrown out.

So, too, was a move to ban or limit smoking at council meetings. Mr Kenneth MacIver, Gress, complained that it was unfair that non-smokers like himself had to suffer the smell of cigarette smoke throughout meetings. He threatened to bring joss-sticks into meetings "and see how you like that".

Mr James MacRae, Stornoway, commented: "Given that he represents North Tolsta, maybe broomsticks would be more appropriate."

31.10.80

No vote on Skye Airstrip sign

"Honest, officer, I was distracted by the sign!"

Attempts at last week's Highland Regional Council meeting in Dingwall to block the raising of the controversial sign at the Isle of Skye airstrip, which includes only token Gaelic wording, were firmly knocked on the head by Mr Ian Campbell, the council convener and himself a Skye representative.

1.2.80

Portree Swimming Pool — a proposed compromise for the Sabbath!

25.1.80

"Honest, officer — we're counting the fish for the Estate!"

South Uist Estates have been accused of hindering a sheltered housing development on the island by imposing restrictive conditions on the sale of 4,000 square metres of land at Howmore to Comhairle nan Eilean.

Among the conditions the estate have imposed on the sale are that the occupiers of the completed houses will not be permitted to own dogs or to keep firearms, shotguns, air rifles or pistols — and that they be liable for any reduction in the number of fish present in the loch.

"Of course, I took them by the scenic route — must have covered 20 miles!"

Last week members and officials of Comhairle nan Eilean learned at first hand a little about the hardships suffered by the people of Rhenigidale in Harris, who have been campaigning for many years for an access road to the remote township.

For the members of the council delegation walked the five-mile rough track to Rhenigidale last Thursday as part of a fact-finding exercise.

24.6.88

27.8.82

"Crisis of conscience" over showing of gay love story

The showing of the much-acclaimed film "My Beautiful Launderette" in Stornoway last year has caused consternation amongst some members of Comhairle nan Eilean's education committee, and some island councillors.

A new Government-produced AIDS informational video for use in schools may not be shown to schoolchildren in the Western Isles. It is understood that a preview of the film by health and community education officials led to calls for it to be banned from island schools.

Those officials who want to see the film banned apparently believe that the open discussion of homosexuality would be unbeneficial for island school children and would be offensive to the religious values of the community.

PEACE CONCERT TO GO AHEAD

"We'd like to know what you're going to waste the money on . . ."

An open-air peace concert is to go ahead next month in the Castle Grounds in Stornoway, despite the dissent of a member of the Stornoway Trust.

Trustee Mr Frank Apps said he would like to know more about the peaceful purposes for which the proceeds were to be used. But the chairman, Mr Sandy Matheson, replied that they were not there to consider the aims and objects of either body, but to consider whether they would make the Castle Grounds available for such a purpose.

The application was granted, although Mr Apps asked that his dissent be recorded.

1.5.81

"Some folk will do anything for publicity!"

The strength of the monarchist sympathies of Skye and Lochalsh District Council was severely tested on Monday, when they considered whether or not to fork out up to £100 of the ratepayers' money for a royal wedding present.

In the end the council agreed to do so — but only thanks to the casting vote of the chairman, Cllr Willie Nicolson, Braes.

27.2.81

"Oh no! Not more bloody toasters!"

15.5.81

"We're only following the orders of the school board, Inspector"

School boards — proposed in a Government consultative document published last week — could lead to a "vociferous few" exerting undue influence over the affairs of a school.

"You better stop, Angus . . . The parents have won the action to stop the school closing!"

Parents fighting to prevent Comhairle nan Eilean closing the small Uist primary schools should know the outcome of their case in the Court of Session tomorrow (Friday). In the meantime, however, the council have begun removing furniture from the threatened schools.

Hundreds of jobs throughout Highland Region and the Western Isles could be at risk if a proposal to end Highlands & Islands Development Board funding for Manpower Services Commission schemes is approved by the Board.

6.6.86

"Any of you know where this museum chappie is?"

The Barra Heritage Society is going a bomb — and that is no overstatement.

A few weeks ago the society, which does not yet have a home of its own, was presented with a bagful of old bits and pieces from Vatersay. The items included a first world war shell.

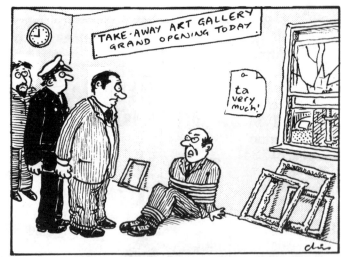

"Unfortunately, someone got the wrong idea!"

Skye & Lochalsh District Council launch their "take-away art gallery" next Friday, 18th July.

A statement issued this week said the scheme was designed to enable people in the district "to enjoy pictures in their homes or at their workplace at very little cost". The council add: "The scheme works like a public library. Local residents can borrow pictures for a period of three months for a charge of £5 per picture, including VAT."

The council's collection to date consists of 13 contemporary prints produced in the four Scottish print workshops in Glasgow, Edinburgh, Aberdeen and Dundee. Among them is a print by Portree artist Tommy MacKenzie entitled "Coruisk".

The prints will be available next Friday from 9.30am and 1pm on a "first-come, first-served basis".

1986

Civil Defence . . .

"And I am proud to announce the appointment of two of the leading experts on nuclear survival technology!"

30.1.81

"You fool! To use that lot in the shelters we'll have to spend another £4,000 on gas masks!"

In a cupboard in Lewis Hospital sit three cases of baked beans, six cases of pilchards, three cases of corned beef and three cases of Tizer (a soft drink). There is lots more besides — a veritable treasure trove of goodies.

these are not, however, just any old baked beans, corned beef, pilchards and Tizer. For this is the cupboard that contains the provisions which will supposedly be used to feed the surviving population of Lewis and Harris in the event of nuclear war.

Council's bombshell scheme for Civil Defence centre

Skye and Lochalsh District Council have come up with a cunning plan to fund the construction of their new office extension on the site of the former drill hall in Portree.

By designating part of the new extension as their Emergency Operations Centre for civil defence purposes the council hope the building will become eligible for a 75 per cent specific grant available from the Scottish Home and Health Department for constructing Civil Defence control centres.

"I don't care what it says in the War Book, councillor MacTaggart, you can't claim your expenses here!"

Although the War Book has undoubtedly been compiled in all seriousness, reading through its 100 chapters is unlikely to be a top priority during the four-minute warning. And although it is reassuring to know that emergency planning officers have devoted time and effort to providing guidance to cope with every eventuality, it is hard to imagine survivors of a nuclear attack looking up Serial 6, Subsection 9(11)(d) to read the comforting words: "Travel allowances/subsistence: Normal local government rates will be paid."

"Ah, constable! Did you bring in the chickens I ordered?"

The plan, said the 'Guardian', suggested the recruitment of 50 special constables to keep order "in addition to an existing list of licensed gun holders will form the volunteer force of armed men to control looting".

The aim of the 100-page plan was "to keep the community going for several months without any outside help". Among the advice given in it is that "chickens have good resistance to radiation and their coops should be brought into the house with enough food and water for 14 days".

24.10.86

18.4.86

"Hello, is that dial-a-prayer?"

12.10.84

"Oh, by the way, Merry Christmas from the sheriff's officers"

The spirit of Christmas

On the first day of Christmas, the council said to me
Send us the money or the lights will go out on your tree

In a spectacular bid for the Spirit of Christmas Award, Comhairle nan Eilean has threatened to set sheriff's officers on a charitable organisation which last year provided a Christmas tree in the town centre.

"Damn Tornadoes! Road hogs!"

"You can take this flags of convenience business too far . . ."

All of CalMac's Minch ferries were tied up in dock on Monday, as a result of the national 24-hour seamen's strike.

The strike was called by the National Union of Seamen as protest action against the shipping line Cunard's insistence on putting two of its three major passenger ships under flags of convenience.

7.11.80

"Calum, the bodach over there says this isn't Uig and we're not on the Heb!"

£12,000 was spent on hiring the MV 'Columba' from CalMac so that guests could have a floating lunch, and another £11,000 was spent to bring a hundred dignitaries up from London on a specially-chartered train.

20.5.83

"We don't know what it is, but it was caught locally and the captain says you've got to use it!"

20.9.85

"Yes, that's right. It's for me and my 12 spouses!"

CHEAPER FARES ON THE WAY!

22.8.80

"Sorry to drop in like this!"

A London property developer has plans to build a holiday home on the Ascrib Islands in Loch Snizort, on Skye's north-west coast. Nothing too unusual about that, perhaps, but Mr Palumbo intends to have his rural retreat *underground!*.

2.5.86

OVERNIGHT BERTHS 1-20

Caledonian MacBrayne have defended the decision not to provide overnight accommodation for travellers on the new ferry vessel 'Hebridean Isles' on the Uig-Tarbert-Lochmaddy route.

8.7.86

The well-loved ferry 'Hebrides' was sold to a company running trips to the Channel Islands.

"These three men were still aboard when we took delivery in 1985, and they say they're not getting off till we reach Tarbert!"

22.11.85

"Sorry mate — they decided it's uneconomical to pay us to collect the tolls after 10.30!"

The regional council have already come out against the idea of a toll bridge, and that is still council policy — although if private investment was the only way to obtain a bridge, it is possible that they might have to accept the idea of a toll.

25.11.88

"I still think it's a bit much selling advertising space on the toilet rolls!"

CalMac will be asked to "examine carefully existing practices, in order to find more efficient and cost-effective ways of delivering the present standard of service".

2.12.88

"According to the Scottish Tourist Board, spring comes early
and autumn comes late. Which d'ye reckon this is?"

"Aye, not only did we tear a good net, but
Eddie here ruined his knife trying to gut it!"

(A torpedo warhead dating from World War One was picked up by the net of a trawler fishing in the Minch last week. It was identified at Dunvegan Pier, and detonated in Loch Dunvegan.)

2.3.79

"Next on the agenda . . . Place your bets for Minch fishing rights!"

23.9.83

Representatives of the French trawler company Jego Quere are likely to meet with a cool reception when they meet fishermen in Kyle on Friday to outline the plan to establish a processing factory there. For the fishermen's blockade of the port last Friday clearly showed their hostility to the French presence. The local regional and district councillors will also attend the meeting.

5.9.80

"What makes you think it's a Danish trawler?"

7.1.83

'ODIN'S RAVEN' BACK ON COURSE

The Viking longship 'Odin's Raven' — which capsized last week in the Sound of Raasay — left Portree on Tuesday to continue her journey to the Isle of Man.

The replica longship is re-enacting a Viking journey from Norway to the Isle of Man millenium celebrations. She was hit by a squall on her way into Portree harbour last Thursday and overturned, throwing the six crew members on board into the sea. They were picked up by a pleasure boat which was carrying a BBC TV crew filming the longship.

Much of the ship's gear was lost overboard, and the crew of Manxmen and Norwegians had to spend the weekend in Skye while awaiting replacement gear.

"Listen, friend! One more crack about Viking submarines . . ."

"It's my new design for a creel buoy — for use during the mackerel season"

20.8.82

A leading authority on the Scottish fish farming industry has alleged that a "protection" racket is going on, over salmon farm leases.

Writing in the current issue of 'Fish Farmer', Dr Ted Needham says he was surprised at first by "the equanimity with which the Crown Estate deal in fish farming rentals had been accepted in some quarters" — among the big companies.

The penny has now dropped, writes Dr Needham. "I deduce that in exchange for rental payments that may exceed £100,000 per annum for the larger companies, they are being offered protection against incomers.

"Once in a site, they and they alone will be able to exploit a whole sea loch to its full potential. Small and local interests will not stand a chance."

6.2.87

"Smile! You're on Candid Camera!"

The spotter plane operated by DAFS from Inverness has caused the fishermen great concern since it was introduced last year. A Skye skipper was recently convicted of illegal fishing after a trial in which photographs taken by the spotter plane were used as key evidence.

1.4.83

Although Lord Mansfield had said the £100,000 to be put back into fish farming represented "something over 10 per cent" of their anticipated income from the industry in Scotland, Mr Graham replied: "When one considers their total income is something in the region of £30 million the percentage to be allocated to the fish farming industry is something like 0.03 per cent."

"Skipper, this chap from the Crown Estate Commissioners wants £100 now or he's going to lift the mooring!"

The Crown Estate Commissioners are planning to extract payments from thousands of boat owners on the west coast who use fixed moorings to anchor their craft in sea lochs and harbours.

"Her Majesty commands me to thank you for the fry, but the rent stays the same."

"Thanks, but I think I might have worked that one out myself . . ."

A Lewis fisherman was left with a red face last week when he unwittingly activated an emergency indicating beacon in a workshop at his house — and the first thing he knew about it was when he heard a rescue helicopter hovering overhead!

Unfortunately, having only received the equipment that day, he was unable to switch the beacon off. The helicopter landed in a nearby field and a crew member deactivated the transmitter for the embarrassed fisherman.

30.5.88

"You are hereby charged with illegal possession of an MK5 Lance Rocket, property of the Ministry of Defence . . ."

"Good job we've got NATO here — otherwise we'd have been over-run by foreign powers!"

16.11.79

"For the last time, sir, I'm telling you our jets don't fly THAT low!"

"You want to complain to the CO about low flying? that's him there, second from the front."

16.9.83

Scottish Women's Rural Institute officials in the West Highlands and Islands this week described as a "lot of rubbish" claims made at the weekend by a Tory MP that the SWRI was being infiltrated by extremists peddling Marxist propaganda.

"Congratulations, Comrade Jessie, on winning the flower arrangement competition!"

28.9.84

Concern over unrestricted shore access for Russian fishermen involved in the mackerel fishery off Ullapool has been dismissed by local people as scaremongering.

The "red alert" was raised by Ross, Cromarty & Skye MP Charles Kennedy, who has written to Home Secretary Douglas Hurd expressing concern about the absence of Customs facilities at Ullapool. The MP thought the Russians should be subjected to immigration controls.

8.11.85

A Ministry of Defence investigation is being carried out following the discovery at a public refuse dump in Portree of classified documents relating to test-firings of torpedoes at the Royal Navy's BUTEC range in the Inner Sound of Raasay.

"I can remember the days when the bin lorries arrived at the dump full and left empty . . ."

6.3.87

"I'm sorry, sir, for some reason every copy of 'Spycatcher'
was lent out within minutes of getting to Ullapool . . ."

Councillor fails in bid to ban "Spycatcher"

A bid to ban the controversial "Spycatcher" book from library shelves in Highland Region failed last week.

"Shh . . . It could be the Free Press . . ."

"Walls have ears" warning

A "walls have ears" message has been issued to workers at the BUTEC range base in Kyle, in a bid to tighten security.

A memo posted on notice boards at the base warns workers that there is a risk of their conversations outside of work being eavesdropped — particularly, it seems, in pubs. They are cautioned not to talk about anything related to their work.

"You fool! You put *next* year's plans up by mistake!"

"We found a great way of getting round the regulations on delivering explosives by sea — *and* testing the alertness of the NATO base!"

Contractors in the Western Isles have claimed that road programmes were being hit as a result of new regulations on the loading and unloading of explosives at ports, and it was forecast that unless supplies of explosives were delivered soon workers could be paid off.

"Oh well, back to the drawing board!"

In a dispatch from St Kilda, our cartoonist Chris has exclusively revealed details of the testing of a new secret weapon being developed by the Army . . . It appears that when food for the Army garrison on the remote island was running short an airdrop was arranged. "Unfortunately," writes Chris, "the pilot was just too accurate — a bag of frozen chickens crashed through the windscreen of a landrover and struck the commanding officer, who was airlifted to hospital in Glasgow with a broken arm and facial injuries." Ah, well, back to the drawing board . . .

16.4.82

"I know you're fed up with undisciplined civilians, sergeants, but don't you think this is going too far?"

Benbecula councillor in clash with army

Benbecula councillor Ray Burnett referred to a sign at the entrance to the base prohibiting the parking of unauthorised vehicles within 25 metres of the perimeter.

This, he said, would mean no parking was allowed in the car park at the airport, by the post office, at the police station or in part of the council's own car park.

20.2.87

"This is the bit that does the actual shredding"

Intergalactic shredder!

What is a "volumatic disintegrator"? That question occurred to Mr Calum Macdonald MP after learning that one is to be installed at the Royal Artillery range in Uist.

Mr Macdonald put down a question asking what the purpose of this fearsome-sounding piece of military hardware might be. The reply explained that a volumatic disintegrator is, in fact, "a large paper-shredding machine"!

12.2.88

One possible solution to the Skye bridge controversy.

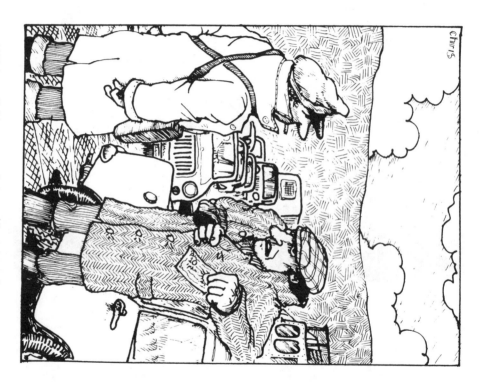

"Wait until they want to bring nuclear waste here — we'll get a bridge quick enough then!"

28.9.79

"Survival is in the eye of the beholder"

A weapons magazine which has been widely criticised in the wake of the Hungerford massacre is promoting the use of "uninhabited islands off Scotland's north-west mainland for "survival exercises" in advance of a nuclear "doomsday".

The magazine, called "Survival Weaponry and Techniques", also carried an advertisement for "survival exercises" in the Cuillins and elsewhere in the Highlands — alongside highly controversial mail order advertisements for guns, crossbows and knives.

"You can't afford to be sentimental — It's been proved beyond a shadow of a doubt that they're responsible for the decline of fish stocks."

16.2.79

"This is a prime example of the sort of damage Friends of the Earth are doing world-wide!"

A move by Small Isles councillor Dr Michael Foxley to give a £50 grant to the environmental watchdog group Friends of the Earth (Scotland) was rejected by Highland Regional councillors on Wednesday.

Referring to the group's record on Dounreay employee councillor Roy Godfrey said: "This organisation has done a considerable amount of damage throughout the world. They have a military wing known as Greenpeace and there is no way we should support them.' Dr Foxley's proposal was rejected by 12-7.

"At least we've got one reason to thankful for Windscale!"

Although the Western Isles and Skye and the west coast has been hit by freezing weather temperatures have been higher here than in most other parts of the country during the past week.

16.1.87

NO CAUSE FOR GROUSING ON THE GLORIOUS 12th

"At least until Chernobyl we were safe till dawn!"

Throughout the Highlands and Islands, there was dancing in the streets when the news came through: "Rifkind Gives Glorious Twelfth Go-Ahead".

A press release issued by the Scottish Office carried the glad tidings to the anxious nation: "There willbe no restrictions imposed on the shooting or sale of grouse as a result of the Chernobyl incident. this was announced today by the Right Honourable Malcolm Rifkind, QC, MP, Secretary of State for Scotland".

Radioactive readings which had been obtained from grouse gave "no cause for concern", said Mr Rifkind, who went on to reveal: "Grouse form a very small part of the diet, a plump bird contains only about six ounces of edible meat, and are generally eaten for only a few months in the year."

In these dark days of mass unemployment and industrial decline, it is pleasing to note that a press release in the name of the Secretary of State for Scotland can still occasionally carry such good and important news.

15.8.86

Island whelks indicted in sex change shocker

"Those island chaps won't touch the smoked salmon — they reckon it's full of TBT"

The Government has moved to ban the use of TBT-based paints by fish farmers and boat owners, in response to a wave of publicity about the alarming impact on shellfish and other marine life.

27.2.87

"When exactly did you start work on the fish farm, Miss Campbell?"

Scientists from the Marine Biological Association at Plymouth have discovered that female dog whelks (Nucella lapillis — not to be confused with the winkle, Littorina littorea) are developing male sex organs as a result of Tributyltin (TBT) pollution. In experiments females whose shells were painted with a spot of the chemical sprouted penises which grew to an alarming length.

18.3.88

The Scottish Office confirmed this week that they regularly monitor the Minch and the western seaboard to check radiation levels.

But members of the group HARM, which launched an appeal for a radiation monitor in Lochalsh last week, are sceptical about the Scottish Office assurances.

Shellfish are not tested because, say the Scottish Office, the water testing is adequate and there is no scientific need to test shellfish. An official said shellfish was not eaten by such large numbers of the population, and although an important industry it does not merit so much attention. But the official gave an assurance that it was "perfectly safe" to eat all Minch shellfish.

"Hold your fire — I only said Merry Christmas!"

Police and SSPCA officers in Portree are this week investigating allegations that a Skye fish-farm manager illegally shot six seals with a shotgun.

"No wonder we never see any corncrakes nowadays — it's these bloody conservationists disturbing them!"

Christmas 1987

**"Never mind, Boss — when you get to the conference you can
tell them you've got Scotland's first flying-fish farm"**

February 1989

Nirex — the Government advisory body on nuclear waste disposal — were due to launch their discussion document on the options for long-term storage of intermediate-level nuclear waste at a meeting in London today. The **Free Press** revealed earlier this year that the British Geological Survey had shortlisted about 30 Scottish islands, several of them around Skye and the Uists, from an original list of over 100 prepared for them by Nirex.

"Of course, our most important piece of equipment here at Nirex — this map and tape measure..."

13.11.87

31.3.89